Questron

Dinosaur world

PSS!

PRICE
STERN
SLOAN

PRICE STERN SLOAN LIMITED, NORTHAMPTON, ENGLAND

The fun way to bring learning to life

This book is specially designed for you to use with Questron, the unique electronic answer wand. Questron contains a magic microchip which senses correct and incorrect answers and replies with 'right' or 'wrong' sounds and lights. It also provides a 'victory' sound and flashing lights when you complete special games or sets of questions.

To start your Questron wand, hold it at this angle and press the tip firmly on the page.

Questron is powered by a 9 volt battery, which should have a very long life since it is activated only when you are looking for an answer. When the battery starts to fail, your wand may malfunction. Replace the battery, making sure it comes from new stock.

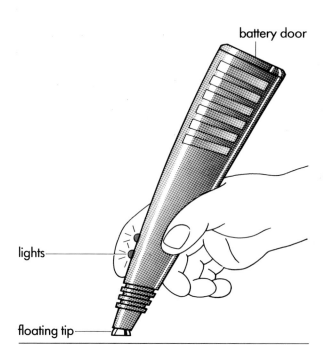

battery door

lights

floating tip

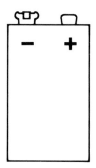

Design   Wagstaffs Design Associates
Compiler   Meyer Solomon
Illustrator Debbie Felts

Printed in Great Britain by Purnell Book Production Limited a member of BPCC plc

Now practise using your wand. Press firmly on the shapes below.

The green light and beep mean 'you are correct'. They will stop when you lift Questron off the page.

The red light and buzzing sound say 'try again'. They will stop when you lift Questron off the page.

The victory sound with flashing lights is a special reward. It will stop when you lift Questron off the page.

TRACK

Press Questron down on START and keep it pressed down as you move to FINISH.

START

FINISH

If you leave the track you will get a buzz. Lift your wand from the page, wait until the sound stops, then start again.

Now you know what your Questron wand can do. Remember, always lift the wand off the page before you move on to the next question.

Dinosaurs become masters of Earth

At one time, Earth was thought to be six thousand years old. Now we believe it is 1 4½ thousand million

years old. Life developed very slowly. First, about 2 thousand million years ago, there were single tiny cells, like microbes. At that time, Earth's air was full of carbon dioxide and other harmful gases. The cells and, later, simple plants called blue-green algae took in the carbon dioxide and gave out

 water oxygen. Very slowly, over hundreds of millions of years, the air gathered plenty of oxygen.

Earth's history of life is divided up into eras slices.

About 600 million years ago, the Palaeozoic Era began. During it, animals developed shells, and fish with bony skeletons inside

their bodies appeared. Some fish with lobe-fins used these to hop about on land, and these fins very slowly turned into legs. The Mesozoic Era began about 225 million years ago. The Mesozoic Era is divided up into three Periods. These are the Triassic Period 225-190 million years ago, the Jurassic Period 190-136 million years ago, and the Cretaceous Period 136-65 million years ago. At the beginning of the Triassic, some reptiles were called

■ thecodonts ■ mastodons.

Their teeth were hollow, very sharp, and grew deep in sockets. From towards the end of the Triassic, right to the

end of the Cretaceous, for about

■ 2 ■ 140 million years,

the dinosaurs were the most successful animals. They died out at the end of the

■ Ice Age ■ Cretaceous Era.

Press Questron on the Thecodont in the picture.

... From a single cell

Some lobe-finned fishes successfully developed their fins into legs, and so were able to walk on land. They developed into amphibians. One such early, Permian, amphibian was a creature called

 Eryops   Ample

These tiny marine plants took in carbon dioxide and gave out oxygen.
They were

 Blue-green algae   Amoeba

The lobe-finned fishes were once thought to have died out completely. But the fossil shown below is still occasionally fished up from the ocean depths.

Press Questron on its name.

 Coelacanth   Salmon

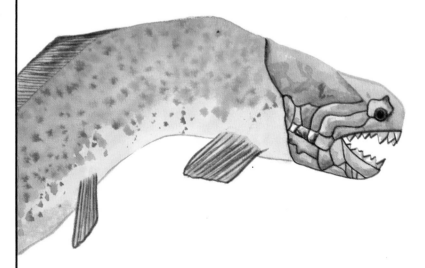

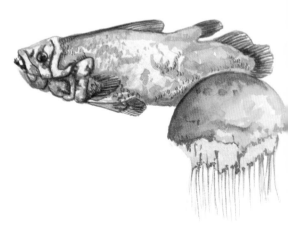

This terrible shark-like creature is called

 Dinichthys   Lockjaw

It was over 9m long. Its huge jaws had enormous teeth.

 Trilobite   Jellyfish   Mouse

One of the above creatures was living around 600 million years ago in the sea.

The mammal-like creature on the right was called

☐ Dimetrodon   ☐ Spiney

It had a large upright 'fin' like corrugated iron. Scientists believe that the animal would warm up very fast by letting the sun shine directly on its fin. When it wanted to keep cooler, it would face into the sun.

Dimetrodon was a Pelycosaur, a reptile that came before the Therapsids. Therapsids were mammal-like creatures.

The creature above is called

☐ Zooey   ☐ Seymouria

It was a midway stage between reptiles and amphibians. It was a little under 1m in length.

In the Triassic Period,

☐ Euparkeria   ☐ Gardenia

arrived. It was about 1m long. It ran on two legs and chased smaller animals. Its teeth were like small daggers. It was a Thecodont, an ancestor of the dinosaurs.

From about 600 million years ago, until now, life on Earth has developed in all kinds of ways. Scientists divide this time into three different Eras. Each Era is divided into Periods.

Press Questron on the Periods during which dinosaurs lived.

600 million
years ago

Palaezoic Era	Mesozoic Era			Cenozoic Era
	Triassic Period	Jurassic Period	Cretaceous Period	

In the picture, a pterodactyl is to the left of a pteranodon. Press Questron on where they are.

After the dinosaurs first appeared, they divided up into two different kinds. In one kind, all the dinosaurs had hip bones that were shaped like those of a bird. So they are called bird-hipped dinosaurs. The word in science for 'bird-hipped' is 'ornitischian'. The other kind of dinosaurs all had hip bones that were shaped like those of a lizard. So they are called lizard-hipped dinosaurs. The word in science for 'lizard-hipped' is 'saurischian'.

The lizard-hipped dinosaurs appeared on Earth before the bird-hipped dinosaurs. Some of the lizard-hipped dinosaurs were meat-eaters, and others were plant-eaters. But all the bird-hipped dinosaurs were plant-eaters.

Press Questron to answer the questions.

How many kinds, or Orders, of dinosaur are there?

 Six   Two

The scientific name for 'bird-hipped' is

 birdippian   ornitischian

The scientific name for 'lizard-hipped' is

 saurischian   lizarus

All the bird-hipped dinosaurs were

 plant-eaters   meat-eaters

Different dinosaurs

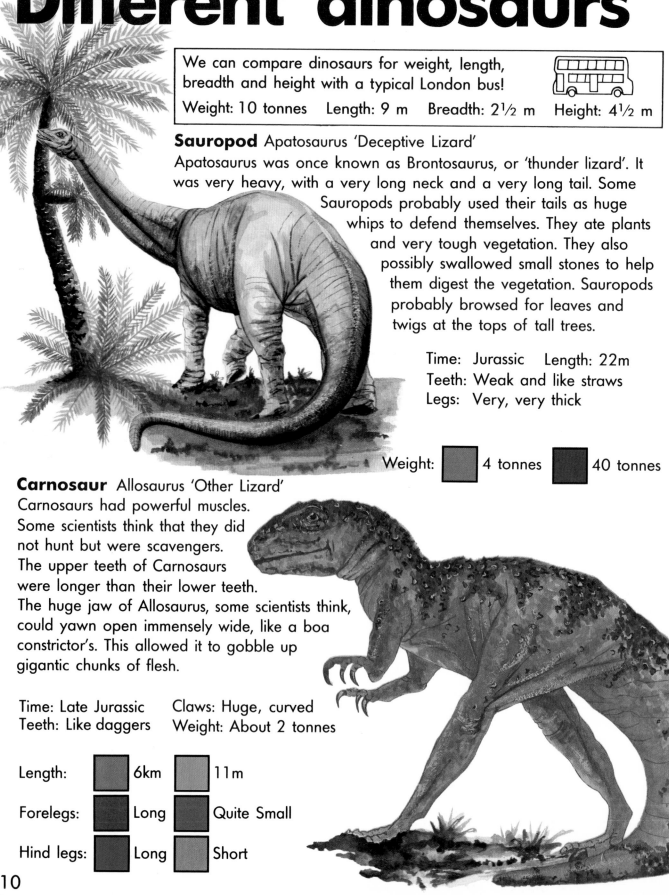

We can compare dinosaurs for weight, length, breadth and height with a typical London bus!

Weight: 10 tonnes   Length: 9 m   Breadth: 2½ m   Height: 4½ m

Sauropod Apatosaurus 'Deceptive Lizard'

Apatosaurus was once known as Brontosaurus, or 'thunder lizard'. It was very heavy, with a very long neck and a very long tail. Some Sauropods probably used their tails as huge whips to defend themselves. They ate plants and very tough vegetation. They also possibly swallowed small stones to help them digest the vegetation. Sauropods probably browsed for leaves and twigs at the tops of tall trees.

Time: Jurassic   Length: 22m
Teeth: Weak and like straws
Legs: Very, very thick

Weight: ☐ 4 tonnes   ☐ 40 tonnes

Carnosaur Allosaurus 'Other Lizard'

Carnosaurs had powerful muscles. Some scientists think that they did not hunt but were scavengers. The upper teeth of Carnosaurs were longer than their lower teeth. The huge jaw of Allosaurus, some scientists think, could yawn open immensely wide, like a boa constrictor's. This allowed it to gobble up gigantic chunks of flesh.

Time: Late Jurassic   Claws: Huge, curved
Teeth: Like daggers   Weight: About 2 tonnes

Length: ☐ 6km   ☐ 11m

Forelegs: ☐ Long   ☐ Quite Small

Hind legs: ☐ Long   ☐ Short

10

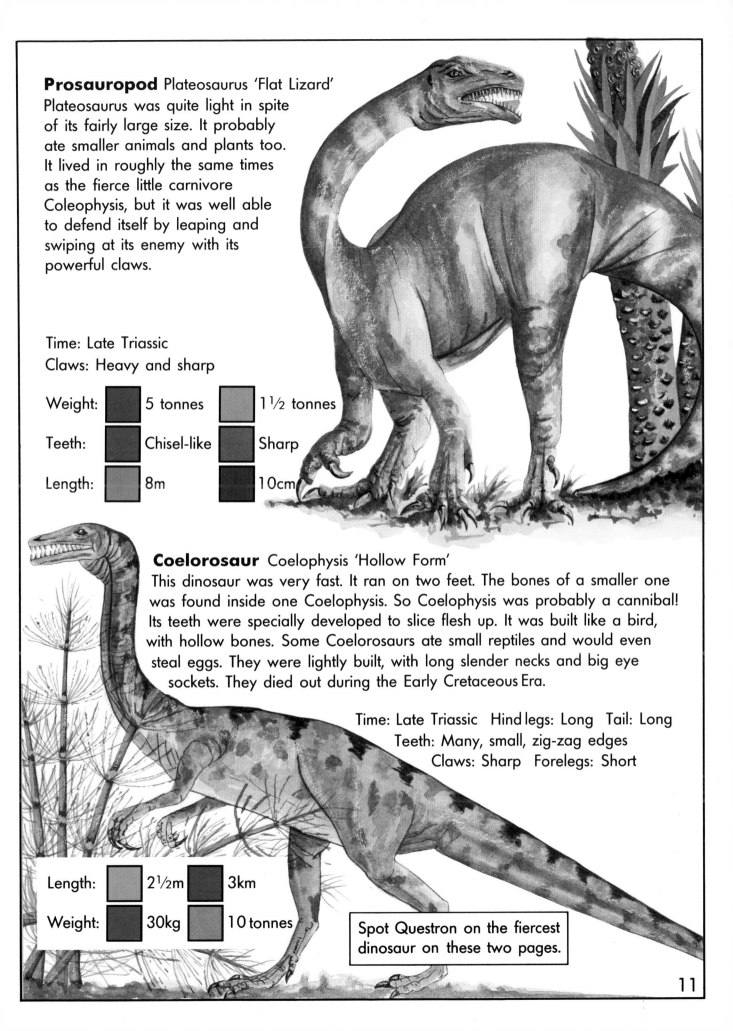

Prosauropod Plateosaurus 'Flat Lizard'
Plateosaurus was quite light in spite
of its fairly large size. It probably
ate smaller animals and plants too.
It lived in roughly the same times
as the fierce little carnivore
Coleophysis, but it was well able
to defend itself by leaping and
swiping at its enemy with its
powerful claws.

Time: Late Triassic
Claws: Heavy and sharp

Weight:		5 tonnes		1½ tonnes
Teeth:		Chisel-like		Sharp
Length:		8m		10cm

Coelorosaur Coelophysis 'Hollow Form'
This dinosaur was very fast. It ran on two feet. The bones of a smaller one
was found inside one Coelophysis. So Coelophysis was probably a cannibal!
Its teeth were specially developed to slice flesh up. It was built like a bird,
with hollow bones. Some Coelorosaurs ate small reptiles and would even
steal eggs. They were lightly built, with long slender necks and big eye
sockets. They died out during the Early Cretaceous Era.

Time: Late Triassic Hind legs: Long Tail: Long
Teeth: Many, small, zig-zag edges
Claws: Sharp Forelegs: Short

Length:		2½m		3km
Weight:		30kg		10 tonnes

Spot Questron on the fiercest
dinosaur on these two pages.

11

Hadrosaur Parasaurolophus ('Next to Saurolophus')

Parasaurolophus had a crest that jutted back over its skull and which was over five feet long. Scientists think that its crest was for showing off to other hadrosaurs! Other scientists think that the crests, being hollow and full of air, were like trumpets that made a sound when Parasaurolophus called to other dinosaurs. Thought to be 'duckbilled', their beaks were actually tough and sharp and used for cutting leaves and branches. Hadrosaurs were practically defenceless. They relied on their eyesight and sense of smell to warn them of danger. Some had as many as 2000 teeth.

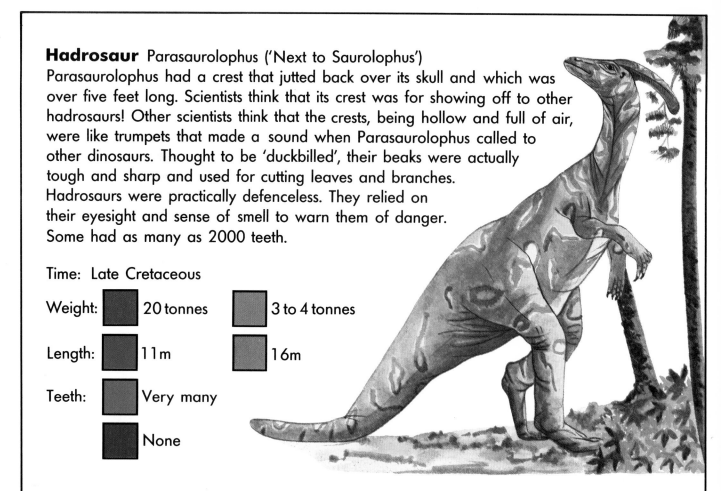

Time: Late Cretaceous

Weight: ■ 20 tonnes   ■ 3 to 4 tonnes

Length: ■ 11m   ■ 16m

Teeth: ■ Very many

■ None

Boneheaded Dinosaur

Pachycephalosaurus ('Thickheaded lizard')
This dinosaur had a very thick, bony and narrow skull. Scientists think that the boneheaded dinosaurs used to butt each other, head-to-head, when they wanted to become leaders of a herd. Boneheaded dinosaurs usually leave only their incredibly thick skulls as fossils. The boneheads are not as well-known as the duckbills.

Time: Late Cretaceous

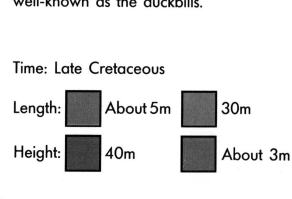

Length: ■ About 5m   ■ 30m

Height: ■ 40m   ■ About 3m

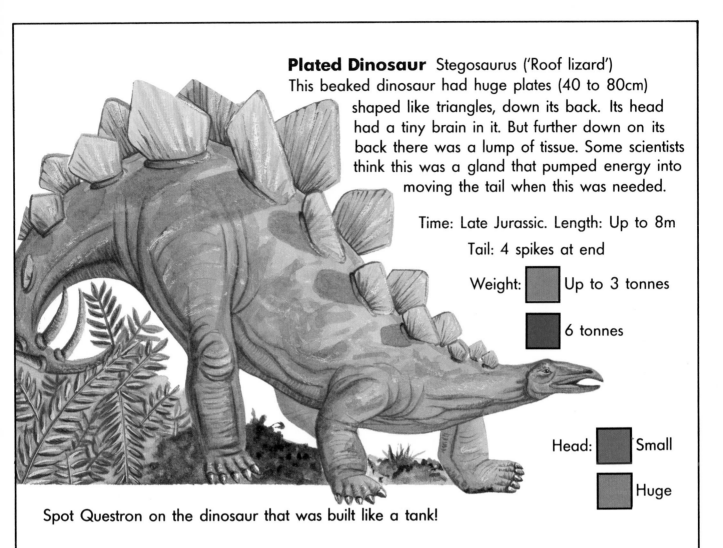

Plated Dinosaur Stegosaurus ('Roof lizard')

This beaked dinosaur had huge plates (40 to 80cm) shaped like triangles, down its back. Its head had a tiny brain in it. But further down on its back there was a lump of tissue. Some scientists think this was a gland that pumped energy into moving the tail when this was needed.

Time: Late Jurassic. Length: Up to 8m

Tail: 4 spikes at end

Weight: Up to 3 tonnes

6 tonnes

Head: Small

Huge

Spot Questron on the dinosaur that was built like a tank!

Armoured Dinosaur Ankylosaurus ('Fused lizard')

This dinosaur was like a low, heavy slab of concrete! It may have been almost impossible to turn over. With bony plate armour on its back and tail and a heavy bone club at the end of its tail, it must have been more than a match for a flesh-eating dinosaur.

Time: Late Cretaceous
Tail: Huge club at end
Teeth: Small

Weight: 10 tonnes | Up to 4 tonnes

Head: Broad and armoured

Tiny

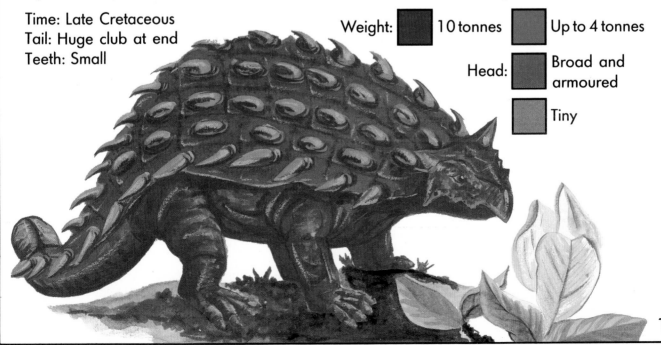

13

Ceratopsian Triceratops ('Three Horns')

This dinosaur was the most dangerous plant-eater of all time. Its huge horns were probably two to three metres long. Its powerful neck muscles could spring its horns upward to spear any attacking dinosaur. Its neck was protected by its backward-pointing collar of bone. The horned dinosaurs were very successful. They seemed to have no enemy that could attack them and easily get away with it.

Time: Late Cretaceous

Head: Huge, about 3 metres long

Length: ☐ 2cm ☐ 11m

Weight: ☐ About 7 tonnes ☐ 22 tonnes   Teeth: ☐ Tough and sharp ☐ Weak

Protoceratops

The ancestor of the horned dinosaurs was a dinosaur now called Protoceratops. It had no horns. Its fossil was discovered by an expedition to Mongolia. The eggs of Protoceratops were found, some with fossils of unhatched babies. Also found were the bodies of a small flesh-eater, Velociraptor, and a Protoceratops, that seemed to have died together while fighting.

The dinosaur on the right is a

☐ Giant Toad

☐ Protoceratops

14

Fossils

When, millions of years ago, a living thing died, it would usually be completely destroyed, leaving no traces. Sometimes, however, it might be covered by layer upon layer of mud or sand very soon after it died. Its soft parts would rot away, but its harder parts might be turned into a stone-like substance with the same shape.

Or it might leave impressions of its ☐ voice ☐ footprints.

Or its ☐ head ☐ tail might drag along the ground and leave its trace.

We know about the dinosaurs because we discover ☐ treasure ☐ fossils.

Even then, because Earth is always moving and changing, heat or pressure or water might still destroy the fossil. But enough fossils have remained for us to be able to find out a lot about the life of the wonderful dinosaurs.

The Earth as you see it now is very different from Earth as it was when the first dinosaurs evolved. At the beginning of the Mesozoic Era, all the huge land masses that we call continents were joined together in one huge super continent that scientists call Pangaea. Then during the 140 million years that the dinosaurs ruled Earth, Pangaea started breaking apart. Scientists can get a good idea as to the shape of the land, long ago, by finding fossils of the same animals in different parts, and at different depths, of the Earth.

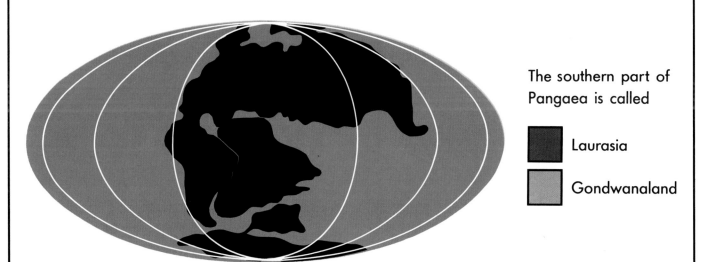

The southern part of Pangaea is called

■ Laurasia

□ Gondwanaland

Press Questron on the part of Pangaea that is now Africa

Dealing with dinosaurs

Palaeontologists are very careful when they take fossils out of the earth.

Press Questron on the tools they use.

- Spade
- Cricket bat
- Pick-and-shovel
- Spoon and fork
- Chisel
- Camera

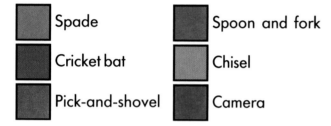

Spot Questron on whatever does not belong in this picture.

The bones are carefully examined and scientists can get a very good idea of how the head, body, and legs were all connected together.

Very often the fossils are in huge blocks of stone. These have to be carefully loaded when they are taken to the museum.

The fossil is wrapped in bandages soaked in

- Plaster of Paris
- a fur coat

The museum workers have to take off the Plaster of Paris carefully. They then have carefully to chip away the bone.

Press Questron on the tools they would use.

- Theodolite
- Microscopes
- Fine brushes
- Hammers
- Telescope
- Chisels

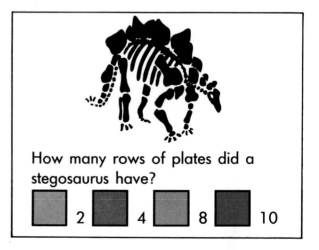

How many rows of plates did a stegosaurus have?

- 2
- 4
- 8
- 10

1	2	3
How many periods were there in the age of the dinosaurs?	Lizard-hipped dinosaurs are known as:	Dimetrodon's sail along its back help[s] its:
3	Saurischia	bala[nce]
6	Ornithischia	temp[erature]
9	carnivores	fligh[t]

Start

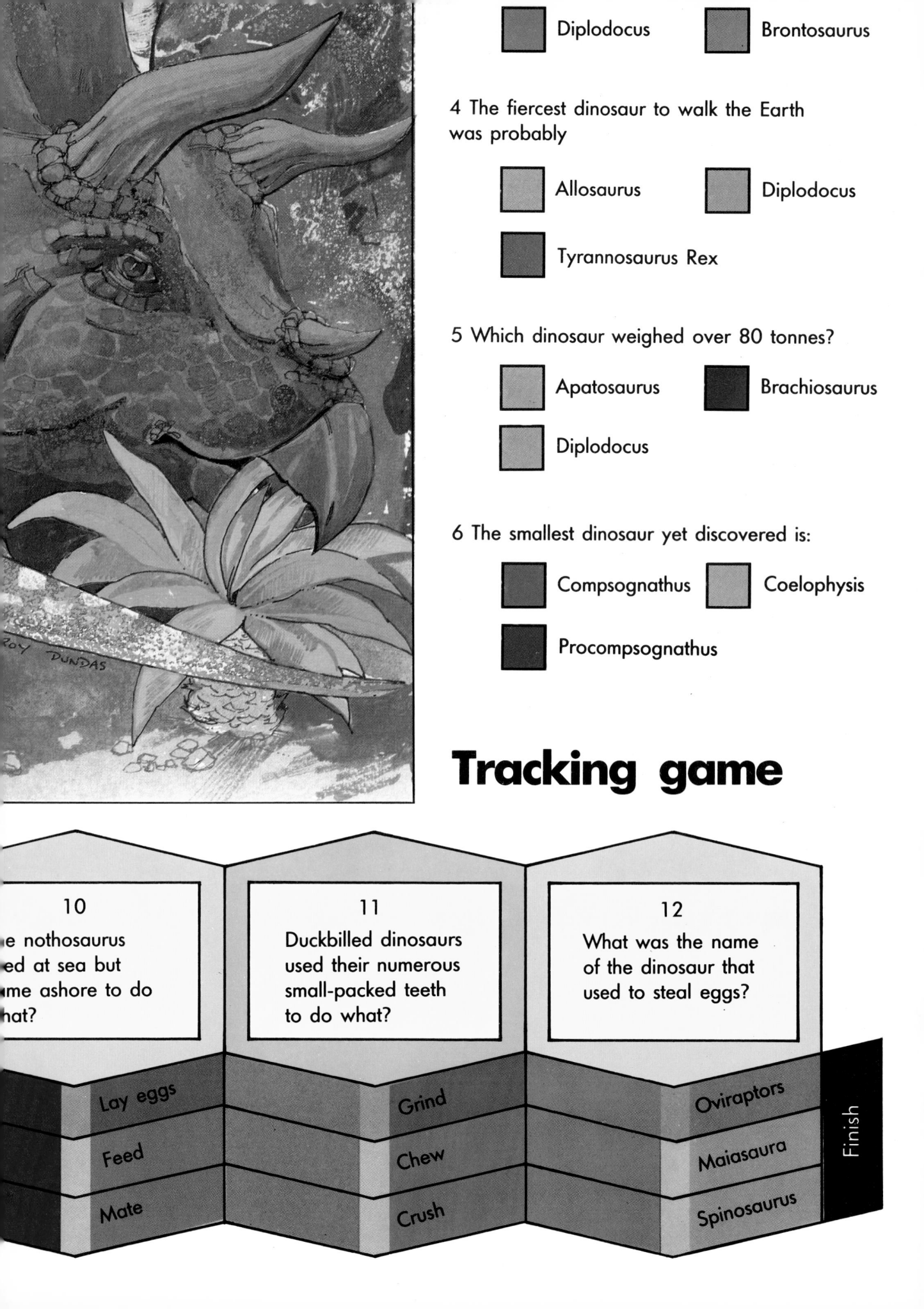

☐ Diplodocus ☐ Brontosaurus

4 The fiercest dinosaur to walk the Earth was probably

☐ Allosaurus ☐ Diplodocus

☐ Tyrannosaurus Rex

5 Which dinosaur weighed over 80 tonnes?

☐ Apatosaurus ☐ Brachiosaurus

☐ Diplodocus

6 The smallest dinosaur yet discovered is:

☐ Compsognathus ☐ Coelophysis

☐ Procompsognathus

Tracking game

10	11	12
e nothosaurus ed at sea but me ashore to do hat?	Duckbilled dinosaurs used their numerous small-packed teeth to do what?	What was the name of the dinosaur that used to steal eggs?
Lay eggs	Grind	Oviraptors
Feed	Chew	Maiasaura
Mate	Crush	Spinosaurus

Finish

Illustrator   Roy Dundas

Dinosaurs

After dominating the Earth for over 140 million years the dinosaurs vanished. Why they disappeared is not really clear. Some scientists think that continental upheavals may have played a part by changing the environment. Another possible answer is that the climate changed.

The warm-blooded mammals were able to adapt to both hot and cold environments and survived.

Although dinosaurs are extinct, many scientists think that birds are descendants of small dinosaurs. What do you think?

◀ Press Questron on the herbivore that was more than a match for a Tyrannosaurus.

Spotting game

1 Diplodocus was probably the largest animal ever known.

 True   False

2 Archaeopteryx is probably the creature that all birds today are descended from.

 True   False

3 The heaviest dinosaur ever to live was probably

4

Plateosaurus had needle-like teeth for eating what?

Leaves

Grass

Flesh

5

Diplodocus used its whiplike tail for fending off what?

Flies

Enemies

Leaves

6

Pachycephalosaurus lived in herds where males fought for:

leadership

mates

friends

7

Stegosaurus' back-plates were used to regulate its:

temperature

breathing

appetite

8

Sharp spikes on the flanks of the Ankylosaurus protects its

legs

belly

teeth

9

The Texas pterosaur had a wingspan of over:

17m

20m

6m

Match the dinosaur

The bones of two dinosaurs are all mixed up. See if you can press Questron on all the bones of Brontosaurus.

Dinosaur detective

Spot Questron on the animals on the right that appear in the pictures below.

All the animals in the pictures are

plant eaters meat eaters

Track Questron to connect the right dinosaur head to the right dinosaur body.

Diplodocus

Iguanadon

Allosaurus

Stegosaurus

Triceratops

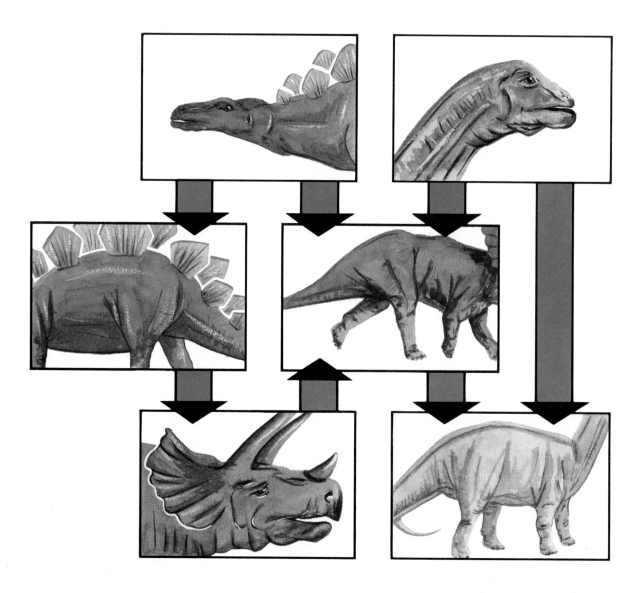

18

Dinosaur deductions

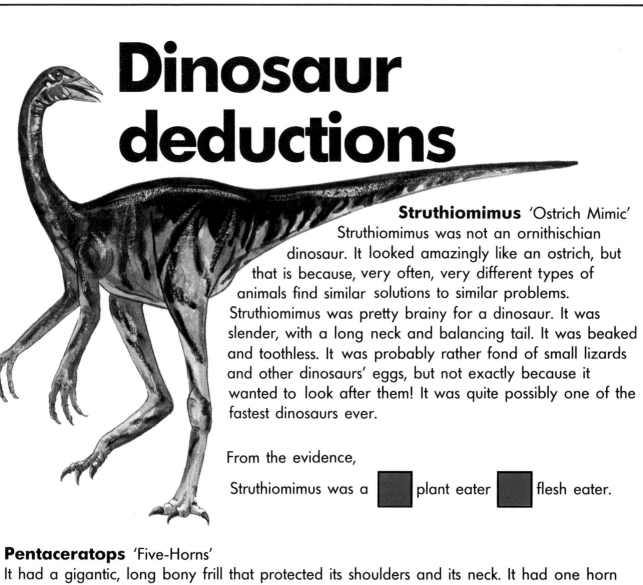

Struthiomimus 'Ostrich Mimic'
Struthiomimus was not an ornithischian dinosaur. It looked amazingly like an ostrich, but that is because, very often, very different types of animals find similar solutions to similar problems. Struthiomimus was pretty brainy for a dinosaur. It was slender, with a long neck and balancing tail. It was beaked and toothless. It was probably rather fond of small lizards and other dinosaurs' eggs, but not exactly because it wanted to look after them! It was quite possibly one of the fastest dinosaurs ever.

From the evidence,

Struthiomimus was a ☐ plant eater ☐ flesh eater.

Pentaceratops 'Five-Horns'
It had a gigantic, long bony frill that protected its shoulders and its neck. It had one horn on its snout, two huge ones just above its eyes, and two smaller ones on each cheek. It had a tough and sharp beak that could cut the leaves of palm trees quite easily. In the time that it lived, the Cretaceous Period, flowering plants had begun to become more and more widespread.

From the evidence, it was a

☐ herbivore ☐ carnivore.

19

Iguanodon 'Lizard Tooth'
When its fossil was first put together, its thumb spike was wrongly put at the tip of its nose! It was nearly as heavy as an elephant. It lived in the Cretaceous Period. It had a heavy balancing tail that was useful when it stood up and put its beaky mouth among the branches of trees. It was bird-hipped.

From the evidence, Ignanodon was a

☐ plant eater   ☐ meat eater

Press Questron on the lizard-hipped dinosaur.

Diplodocus 'Double Beam'
Diplodocus had a very long neck and a very long tail. Its tail could be used to whip around and strike an attacking dinosaur. Its teeth were peg-like and weak, and so probably would not bite hard. It was lizard-hipped. Its legs were quite slender, but were strong enough to support its body weight, although it was not as heavy as the Apatosaurus. It was one of the longest dinosaurs ever. It was nearly 28m long. It weighed about 11 tonnes and lived during late Jurassic times.

From the evidence, Diplodocus was a

☐ herbivore   ☐ carnivore

20

Deinonychus 'Terrible Claw'
Deinonychus had a stiff tail
supported by bony rods. It had
excellent balance. On each foot it had a
huge curved claw about 13cm long. When
it walked, it could move the terrible claw up
out of the way. It could jump and slash at
the stomach of another dinosaur, and rip it. Its
forefeet were very much like arms designed
specially to hug its victims. It lived in the Cretaceous
Era. It was light, and was round about 3m long.
It was lizard-hipped. Its sense of sight and smell
were very keen. It had a fairly big brain.

From the evidence, Deinonychus was a

flesh eater   plant eater

Press Questron on the dinosaur
which could attack while
standing on one leg.

Tyrannosaurus Rex 'King of the Tyrant Lizards'
It was lizard-hipped. It was immense. It lived in the late Cretaceous Era.
It had huge, curved teeth. It had thick legs and was two-footed. Its arms
were so small, they could hardly reach its mouth. It had strong, sharp,
heavy, tearing claws on its hands and
enormous talons on each foot. It was
over 12m long, nearly 6m high, and
was heavier than any elephant.
Its head was huge, and its curved
teeth about 19cm long. It could
gape its mouth very wide open
and snap it quickly shut.

From the evidence, Tyrannosaurus Rex

was a   plant eater   meat eater

21

Fossil facts

- Most of the dinosaurs were herbivores. The larger dinosaurs lived from 75 to 150 years.
- All the flesh-eating dinosaurs were two-footed. All flesh-eaters were lizard-hipped, though there were also lizard-hipped plant-eaters.
- Saurischian dinosaurs usually had their front limbs shorter than their rear limbs. The exception was the giant herbivore Brachiosaurus, which was one of the most gigantic dinosaurs that have ever walked the Earth. Its front limbs were longer than its rear limbs. It was over 25m long, as high as a four-storey building, and heavier than 20 elephants.

Build a dinosaur

Press Questron on the four pieces that belong to the Iguanodon on the right.

The Iguanodon had no teeth.

☐ False ☐ True

Dinosaur detective

Three fossil specimens of dinosaurs have been discovered. You call them TRACY, AL and DENNIS for the time being. The table below gives what might be true about each specimen. Questron will beep if a fact in the table is true. It will buzz if it is not.

	TRACY		AL		DENNIS	
Teeth	Sharp	■	Like daggers	■	Weak	■
	Blunt	■	Blunt	■	Sharp	■
Claws	Strong	■	Blunt	■	Small	■
	Weak	■	Very Sharp	■	Curved, sharp and retractable	■
Tail	Medium	■	Heavy	■	Short	■
	Clubbed	■	Light	■	Stiff and Long	■
Head	Three Horns	■	Light	■	Heavy	■
	Armoured	■	Massive	■	Light	■
Pelvis	Bird-like	■	Lizard-like	■	Bird-like	■
	Lizard-like	■	Bird-like	■	Lizard-like	■

From the evidence: DENNIS is possibly a ■ Deinonychus   ■ Diplodocus

AL is possibly a ■ plant eater   ■ flesh eater

TRACY is possibly a ■ Triceratops   ■ Allosaurus

23

True or false

A hadrosaur-type dinosaur is called Maiasaura. Its name means 'good mother lizard'. This is because palaeontologists found a nest with little babies in it. Some of them think this shows that, just like birds do, it brought food to feed its babies with.

True   False

Scientists can get a good idea of how fast an animal can walk or run just by examining footprints. They measure things like the length of the stride and the pace.
These measurements showed that some dinosaurs could run as fast as 40 miles per hour.
Scientists can also make an estimate of the size of a dinosaur by counting its vertebrae and measuring their sizes.

True   False

Press Questron on the Allosaurus.

Not true, because these animals lived at different times.

 Yes   No

A flesh-eating Spinosaurus met a Dimetrodon on a warm day in the Jurassic Period. They were fighting each other to a standstill until an Allosaurus came along and broke up the fight.

24

Track Questron through the paths with the correct answers.

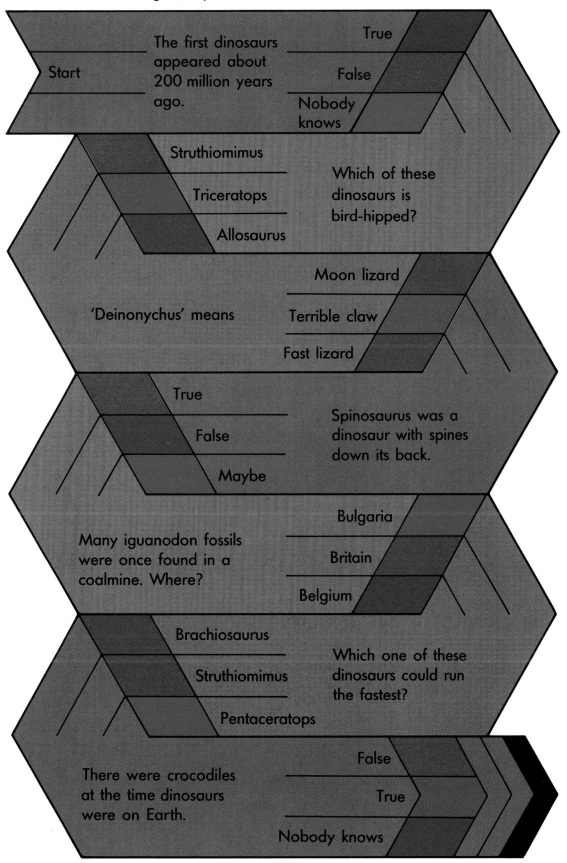

Start

The first dinosaurs appeared about 200 million years ago.

True

False

Nobody knows

Struthiomimus

Triceratops

Allosaurus

Which of these dinosaurs is bird-hipped?

Moon lizard

Terrible claw

Fast lizard

'Deinonychus' means

True

False

Maybe

Spinosaurus was a dinosaur with spines down its back.

Bulgaria

Britain

Belgium

Many iguanodon fossils were once found in a coalmine. Where?

Brachiosaurus

Struthiomimus

Pentaceratops

Which one of these dinosaurs could run the fastest?

There were crocodiles at the time dinosaurs were on Earth.

False

True

Nobody knows

Time traveller

You are a Time Traveller, and you have to travel through the Jurassic and Cretaceous periods before you are able to use your Time Machine again to get back in time for dinner. You will have to track your way through, avoiding flesh-eating dinosaurs, and only meeting (at a safe distance!) plant-eating dinosaurs, until you find a safe exit.

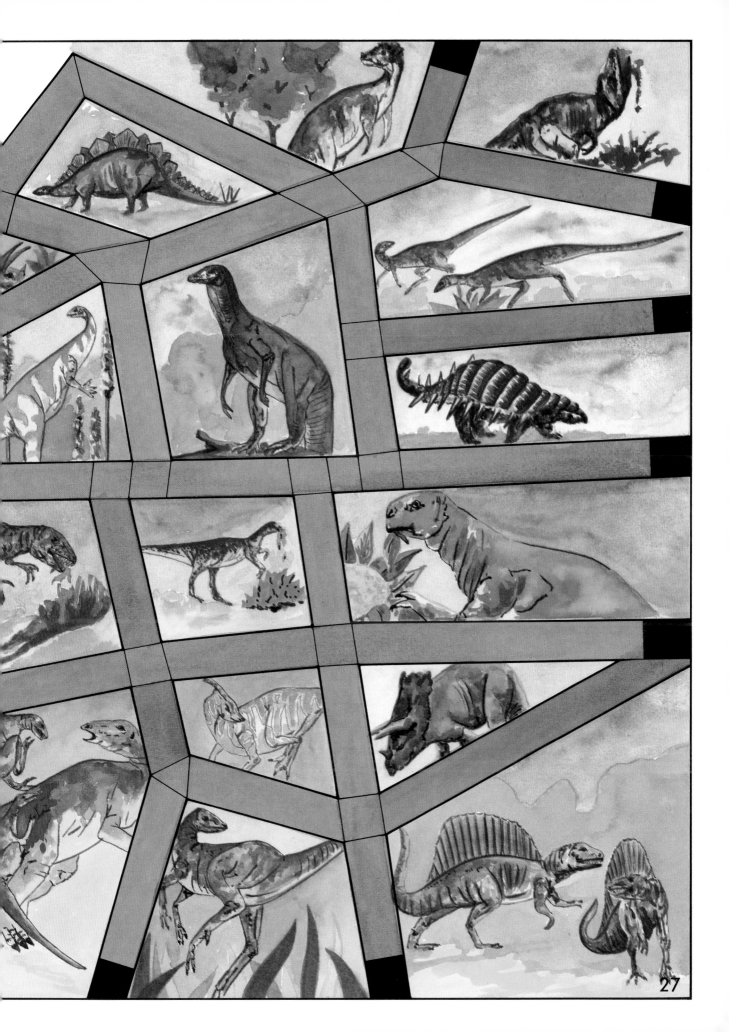

27

Dinosaur wars

Diplodocus walked in the swamp, with just its head above the water. It was trying to drown the parasites that were burrowing into its scaly skin, and the insects that were buzzing around its eyes. It was a warm, humid day in Jurassic times. As Diplodocus moved through the water, it fed on plants. Although it was very long it was quite light.

It slowly pulled its 28m length to dry land. It walked on solid legs. It lifted its head and used its peg-like teeth to rake leaves and nuts from the top of the trees. Its eyes and nostrils were near the top of its head, so that leaves and branches did not scrape them. The sauripod herbivore Diplodocus snipped most of the leaves from the cycad tree. Its neck had become a bit tired, so it lowered its head. It saw a log that had fallen to the ground and walked to it to sniff it to see if it had any tasty branches

left on it. All of a sudden there was a mighty roar. The log was really an Allosaurus.

The herbivore in the story is called

☐ Triceratops ☐ Diplodocus

It lived in which times?

☐ Cretaceous ☐ Jurassic

The 'log' it saw was really

☐ Allosaurus ☐ Triceratops

Allosaurus was a

☐ plant eater ☐ flesh eater

Allosaurus used its short front legs to push itself up to its terrible 6m height. But by the time Allosaurus was ready to strike, Diplodocus had turned and was running towards the water on all its 4 feet. Allosaurus took almost a minute to realise what had happened. The two dinosaurs ran, both of them holding their tails high for better balance. The 11m long Allosaurus chased the 28m Diplodocus.

Allosaurus was catching up with Diplodocus! Diplodocus stopped and moved sideways. The sharp greedy eyes of Allosaurus gleamed. Its huge jaws opened wide, showing its razor-sharp teeth. It plunged its head down and bit Diplodocus on its back. A few of its teeth snapped off inside the tough scaly skin of Diplodocus. But at the same time the Diplodocus whipped its tail around and smashed the leg of the Allosaurus. The Allosaurus fell down, crippled. Diplodocus ran off to join its herd. An interested watcher of the battle was Coelurus. It was hidden behind a tree.

It waited until the Allosaur's roars of pain stopped, and Allosaurus lay still. Then, it was joined by other members of its pack. Together they ran and jumped on Allosaurus and began feeding on it.

Allosaurus had a jaw that could open wide.

 True   False

Diplodocus had a very long, whiplike

 claw   tail

Coelurus was a small, flesh-eating

 mammal   dinosaur

Some dinosaurs would feed on the bodies of already dead animals.

 True   False

Spot Questron on the giant dragonfly in one of the pictures on these pages.

29

Extinction

What caused all the dinosaurs to die ?

Scientists were extremely puzzled, when examining the fossil records, to see that there were no traces of dinosaurs at the end of the Cretaceous, 65 million years ago. Something terrible must have happened — a disaster of the first magnitude. It wasn't only the dinosaurs that suffered, either. Sea life, such as ammonites, and pterosaurs were also wiped out. Of course, over 140 million years, many different types of dinosaurs had already died out. But many had remained,

and these were now to die.

There are many theories as to why this happened. But none of them are really proven. Some scientists think a Death Star comes around every 26 million years and causes comets to move out of their usual path. A comet or asteroid may then crash into Earth. In fact, there have been mass extinctions before the Cretaceous in Earth's history. Other scientists think that there was a change in the climate. It got much colder. Yet other scientists think that small mammals stole and ate the dinosaur eggs. Huge volcanic eruptions may have poured dust into the atmosphere. The Earth has a layer of ozone protecting the atmosphere. This was destroyed, and harmful radiation

from the Sun destroyed the dinosaurs. Some scientists think that the parts of Earth where dinosaurs ruled became connected again to parts where there were different types of animals. These animals moved in. They carried parasites and disease which the dinosaurs could not deal with. The balance of life on which the dinosaurs and many other animals depended was upset, but animals such as the small mammals were able to survive. One more theory is that, because the oxygen content of the air changed, the dinosaurs could not breathe properly anymore, and so died out.

Press Questron on the correct choices in the questions.

The Death Star may come round every

☐ 2 million ☐ 26 million years.

The Earth's atmosphere has a protective layer of

☐ kerosene ☐ ozone

Huge volcanic eruptions might have filled the atmosphere with

☐ dust ☐ lava

Dinosaurs died out at the end of the

☐ Jurassic ☐ Cretaceous Era

Dinosaur facts

A plateosaurus lived in the time called?

 Jurassic

Late Jurassic

 Late Triassic

 Late Cretaceous

We believe the Earth to be how many thousand million years old?

 6

10

 2

 4½

Tiny marine plants that took in carbon dioxide and gave out oxygen were called

 Blue-green algae

Amoeba

 Jellyfish

 Dinichthys

Most of the dinosaurs were

 Carnivore

Herbivore

 Saurischian

 Coelosaur

The larger dinosaurs lived from

 75-150 years

25-50 years

 200-350 years

 10-25 years

Tyrannosaurus Rex was how many metres long?

 7

5

 12

 4